Be Quiet!

Alison Hawes

Illustrated by Ben Cort

RIGBY

Jack and his dad went
to the cinema.
Dad got the tickets.

Jack got the popcorn and the drinks.

The film began.
"I like this film," said Jack.
"I like the rockets. Whoosh!"

"Shhhh!" everyone said.

Jack crunched his popcorn.
"I like this popcorn," he said.

"Shhhh!" everyone said.

Jack slurped his drink.
"I like this drink," he said.

"Shhhh!" everyone said.

Jack got up. He wanted to
go to the toilet.

"Shhhh!" everyone said.

Then Jack saw a friend.
"Hello Ben," he said.

"**Be quiet!**" everyone said.

The film ended.
Everyone got up to go.

"Come on, Dad," said Jack, but Dad was asleep.

"Shhhh everyone!
My dad's asleep," said Jack.